JANE MOERSCHEL

Jane Moerschel is a biologist who has worked in cancer research for the past twenty-one years. She has recently retired from her position as a Clinical Research Assistant for a Clinical Oncology Program. Ms. Moerschel attended the University of Missouri and Central Missouri State University where she received a Bachelor of Science Degree in Biology.

MARY DRAKESMITH

Mary Drakesmith is a registered nurse who has worked in the medical field for over twenty years. She is a graduate of St. Louis University with a Bachelor of Science in Nursing. She has also been an instructor of nursing for seven years at local colleges. She is presently employed as a Clinical Research Assistant for a Community Clinical Oncology Program.

Preface

It is an ironic truth that most people avoid thinking about one of the unavoidable facts of life—their own mortality. In our years of work in the cancer research department of a major medical center, we have seen first-hand what people go through at the end of life. Many find peace and well being when they take the time to arrange their personal business and deal with family issues.

But not everyone knows when the end is near. With a sudden death, those left behind can find their grief compounded by the confusion of handling the person's daily affairs. Even such basic things as finding a safety deposit box key, paying the electric bill, or knowing which lawyer to call about the will can seem overwhelming.

Since no one knows when life will end, we believe it is important to organize your affairs on a continuing basis. Our book is designed to be a practical workbook that will help you catalog your important documents and personal belongings. It does not take the place of a will or legal counsel.

Our own experiences of going through this transition from life to death with a loved one has made us realize the importance of having all matters in order to emotionally and intellectually enhance the survivor's role to continue on the journey in life.

Jane Moerschel
Mary Drakesmith

WHEN I LEAVE
AND
YOU ARE LEFT:

A Book to Help You Organize
Your Personal Affairs

MARY M. DRAKESMITH

JANE R. MOERSCHEL

This book was completed by

Name _____

Maiden Name _____

Address _____

_____

Social Security # _____

Birth Date _____

Place of Birth _____

How To Use This Book

1. Complete each section in pencil so that you can regularly update information.

2. Fill in each section as completely as possible. The more information you give, the better the chances are that your wishes will be followed.

3. After filling out each section, place the book in a safe place. Communicate to your loved ones the location of the book. If you have chosen a locked box, make sure that someone will know the location of the key.

TABLE OF CONTENTS

I

PERSONAL DATA

This section identifies the family and
friends I want you to contact
immediately, as well as the professionals
who care for me and my home.

I. PERSONAL DATA

Date of Birth _____

Place of Birth _____

_____

Occupation or previous occupation _____

_____

Business or previous business _____

_____

Religious affiliation _____

_____

Elementary school (name) _____

High school (name) _____

College (name) _____

Spouse/Significant Other _____

Address _____

_____ Phone _____

Mother _____

Address _____

_____ Phone _____

Father _____

Address _____

_____ Phone _____

Child _____

Address _____

_____ Phone _____

Child _____

Address _____

_____ Phone _____

Child _____

Address _____

_____ Phone _____

Child _____

Address _____

_____ Phone _____

Child _____

Address _____

_____ Phone _____

Sister _____

Address _____

_____ Phone _____

Sister _____

Address _____

_____ Phone _____

Sister _____

Address _____

_____ Phone _____

Sister _____

Address _____

_____ Phone _____

Brother _____

Address _____

_____ Phone _____

Brother _____

Address _____

_____ Phone _____ _____

Brother _____

Address _____

_____ Phone _____

Brother _____

Address _____

_____ Phone _____

Relative _____

Address _____

_____ Phone _____

Relative _____

Address _____

_____ Phone _____

Relative _____

Address _____

_____ Phone _____

Relative _____

Address _____

_____ Phone _____

CLOSE
FRIENDS

Name _____

Address _____

_____ Phone _____

Name _____

Address _____

_____ Phone _____

<u>CLOSE</u> <u>FRIENDS</u> - (Continued)	Name _____ Address _____ _____ Phone _____
	Name _____ Address _____ _____ Phone _____
	Name _____ Address _____ _____ Phone _____
	Name _____ Address _____ _____ Phone _____
<u>DOCTORS</u>	Name _____ Address _____ _____ Phone _____
	Name _____ Address _____ _____ Phone _____
	Name _____ Address _____ _____ Phone _____
<u>DENTIST</u>	Name _____ Address _____ _____ Phone _____
<u>OTHERS</u> <u>TO</u> <u>CONTACT</u>	Name _____ Address _____ _____ Phone _____

Name _____

Address _____

_____ Phone _____

Name _____

Address _____

_____ Phone _____

Name _____

Address _____

_____ Phone _____

Name _____

Address _____

_____ Phone _____

NOTES

NOTES

NOTES

II

FUNERAL

I have given careful consideration to planning my funeral. Please observe the following preferences.

II. FUNERAL

MORTUARY	Name _____
	Address _____
	_____ Phone _____
CHURCH	Name _____
	Address _____
	_____ Phone _____
CLERGY	Name _____
	Address _____
	_____ Phone _____
FUNERAL SERVICE	Type of service _____
	_____
	_____
	_____
	Pall bearer _____
	Address _____
	_____ Phone _____
	Pall bearer _____
	Address _____
	_____ Phone _____
	Pall bearer _____
	Address _____
	_____ Phone _____
	Pall bearer _____
	Address _____
	_____ Phone _____

Pall bearer _____

Address _____

_____ Phone _____

Pall bearer _____

Address _____

_____ Phone _____

Usher _____

Address _____

_____ Phone _____

Usher _____

Address _____

_____ Phone _____

Usher _____

Address _____

_____ Phone _____

Usher _____

Address _____

_____ Phone _____

Music

Name _____

Address _____

_____ Phone _____

Music

Name _____

Address _____

_____ Phone _____

Flower distribution

Name _____

Address _____

_____ Phone _____

Flower distribution

Name _____

Address _____

_____ Phone _____

Flower distribution

Name _____

Address _____

_____ Phone _____

Flower distribution

Name _____

Address _____

_____ Phone _____

Charity donations

Name _____

Address _____

_____ Phone _____

Charity donations

Name _____

Address _____

_____ Phone _____

Charity donations

Name _____

Address _____

_____ Phone _____

OBITUARY
_____
_____
_____
_____
_____
_____
_____
_____
_____
_____
_____
_____
_____
_____

SPECIAL
REQUESTS

Casket (type) _____

Casket (open or closed) _____

Burial _____

Cremation _____

Burial attire _____
_____

Jewelry _____
_____

CEMETERY

Name _____

Address _____

_____ Phone _____

Deed location _____

Plot in name of _____

Section _____

Plot number _____

Block _____

NOTES

NOTES

III

<u>IMMEDIATE CONTACTS</u>
<u>AND RESOURCES</u>

The experts and institutions named here
are critical to planning my funeral and
settling my household affairs.

III. IMMEDIATE CONTACTS AND RESOURCES

EXECUTOR OF WILL

Name _____

Address _____

_____ Phone _____

ATTORNEY

Name _____

Address _____

_____ Phone _____

BANKS

Name _____

Address _____

_____ Phone _____

Name _____

Address _____

_____ Phone _____

Name _____

Address _____

_____ Phone _____

Name _____

Address _____

_____ Phone _____

SAFE DEPOSIT & KEYS

Bank _____

Address _____

_____ Phone _____

Bank _____

Address _____

_____Phone _____

SOCIAL
SECURITY

Office address _____

Phone _____ Social security# _____

VETERANS
ADMINI-
STRATION

Name _____

Address _____

_____ Phone _____

EMPLOYER

Name _____

Address _____

_____ Phone _____

Name _____

Address _____

_____ Phone _____

UTILITY
COMPANIES

Gas company _____

Address _____

_____ Phone _____

Electric company _____

Address _____

_____ Phone _____

Water/sewer company _____

Address _____

_____ Phone _____

Phone company _____

Mobile phone company _____

Long distance company _____

Cable TV company _____

_____

_____

_____

NOTES

NOTES

NOTES

IV

<u>DOCUMENT LOCATIONS</u>

To avoid a "paper chase," I have listed
the location of all my personal
documents.

IV. DOCUMENT LOCATIONS

BANK
STATEMENTS

BOND
CERTIFICATES

STOCK
CERTIFICATES

INSURANCE
POLICIES AND
ANNUITIES

RETIREMENT
AND PENSION
POLICIES

LOAN
DOCUMENTS

CREDIT CARD
COMPANIES

AUTOMOBILE
TITLES

_____

PROPERTY
DEEDS

_____

TAX
RETURNS

_____

BIRTH
CERTIFICATE

_____

CITIZENSHIP
DOCUMENTS

_____

MILITARY
DOCUMENTS

_____

MARRIAGE
CERTIFICATE

_____

DIVORCE
DOCUMENTS

_____

POWER OF
ATTORNEY

_____
_____
_____

LIVING
WILL

_____
_____
_____

WILL

_____
_____
_____

TRUSTS

_____
_____
_____

OTHER
INVESTMENT
DOCUMENTS

(Certificates
of deposit,
money market
accounts,
annuities)

_____
_____
_____

_____
_____
_____

_____
_____
_____

OTHER INVESTMENT DOCUMENTS -

Continued

NOTES

NOTES

NOTES

V

<u>FINANCES</u>

This section identifies money coming in
and bills that need to be paid.
In addition, you will find a cataloging of
my assets and investments.

V. FINANCES

INCOME

Source _____
Address _____
_____ Phone _____
Amount _____

Source _____
Address _____
_____ Phone _____
Amount _____

Source _____
Address _____
_____ Phone _____
Amount _____

Source _____
Address _____
_____ Phone _____
Amount _____

Source _____
Address _____
_____ Phone _____
Amount _____

Source _____
Address _____
_____ Phone _____
Amount _____

Name _____

Address _____

_____ Phone _____

Name _____

Address _____

_____ Phone _____

Name _____

Address _____

_____ Phone _____

Name _____

Address _____

_____ Phone _____

Name _____

Address _____

_____ Phone _____

Name _____

Address _____

_____ Phone _____

Name _____

Address _____

_____ Phone _____

Name _____

Address _____

_____ Phone _____

Name _____

Address _____

_____ Phone _____

RETIREMENT PROGRAMS

(Pensions, IRAs, Self-employment Plans, Keogh Plans)

Name _____

Address _____

_____ Phone _____

Name _____

Address _____

_____ Phone _____

Name _____

Address _____

_____ Phone _____

Name _____

Address _____

_____ Phone _____

Name _____

Address _____

_____ Phone _____

Name _____

Address _____

_____ Phone _____

Name _____

Address _____

_____ Phone _____

Name _____

Address _____

_____ Phone _____

Name _____

Address _____

_____ Phone _____

**REAL
ESTATE**

Address _____

_____

Address _____

_____

Address _____

_____

Address _____

_____

Address _____

_____

Address _____

_____

Address _____

_____

Address _____

_____

Address _____

_____

Address _____

_____

Address _____

_____

Address _____

_____

Address _____

_____

Address _____

_____

Address _____

_____

(Held with broker)

Broker name _____

Address _____

_____ Phone _____

Broker name _____

Address _____

_____ Phone _____

Broker name _____

Address _____

_____ Phone _____

Broker name _____

Address _____

_____ Phone _____

Broker name _____

Address _____

_____ Phone _____

Broker name _____

Address _____

_____ Phone _____

Broker name _____

Address _____

_____ Phone _____

Broker name _____

Address _____

_____ Phone _____

Broker name _____

Address _____

_____ Phone _____

STOCKS
(Individually held)

Company name _____

Certificate number_____Number of shares _____

Company name _____

Certificate number_____Number of shares _____

Company name _____

Certificate number_____Number of shares _____

Company name _____

Certificate number_____Number of shares _____

Company name _____

Certificate number_____Number of shares _____

Company name _____

Certificate number_____Number of shares _____

Company name _____

Certificate number_____Number of shares _____

Company name _____

Certificate number_____Number of shares _____

Company name _____

Certificate number_____Number of shares _____

Company name _____

Certificate number_____Number of shares _____

Company name _____

Certificate number_____Number of shares _____

Company name _____

Certificate number_____Number of shares _____

Company name _____

Certificate number_____Number of shares _____

BONDS

Type of bond _____

Amount _____

Type of bond _____

Amount _____

Type of bond _____

Amount _____

Type of bond _____

Amount _____

Type of bond _____

Amount _____

Type of bond _____

Amount _____

Type of bond _____

Amount _____

Type of bond _____

Amount _____

Type of bond _____

Amount _____

Type of bond _____

Amount _____

Type of bond _____

Amount _____

Type of bond _____

Amount _____

Type of bond _____

Amount _____

ANNUITIES

Insurer _____

Certificate Number _____

Insurer _____

Certificate Number _____

Insurer _____

Certificate Number _____

Insurer _____

Certificate Number _____

Insurer _____

Certificate Number _____

Insurer _____

Certificate Number _____

Insurer _____

Certificate Number _____

Insurer _____

Certificate Number _____

Insurer _____

Certificate Number _____

Insurer _____

Certificate Number _____

Insurer _____

Certificate Number _____

Insurer _____

Certificate Number _____

CHECKING ACCOUNTS

(Banks, credit unions, savings & loans)

Name _____

Address _____

_____ Account No. _____

Name _____

Address _____

_____ Account No. _____

Name _____

Address _____

_____ Account No. _____

Name _____

Address _____

_____ Account No. _____

Name _____

Address _____

_____ Account No. _____

Name _____

Address _____

_____ Account No. _____

Name _____

Address _____

_____ Account No. _____

Name _____

Address _____

_____ Account No. _____

Name _____

Address _____

_____ Account No. _____

SAVINGS
ACCOUNTS

Name _____

Address _____

_____ Account No. _____

Name _____

Address _____

_____Account No. _____

Name _____

Address _____

_____Account No. _____

Name _____

Address _____

_____Account No. _____

Name _____

Address _____

_____Account No. _____

"HIDDEN
CASH"

Location _____

_____

_____

Location _____

_____

_____

Location _____

_____

_____

Location _____

_____

_____

OTHER INVESTMENTS

(Certificates of deposit, money market)

Company _____

Address _____

_____

Company _____

Address _____

_____

Company _____

Address _____

_____

Company _____

Address _____

_____

Company _____

Address _____

_____

Company _____

Address _____

_____

Company _____

Address _____

_____

Company _____

Address _____

_____

Company _____

Address _____

_____

Company _____

Address _____

_____

Company _____

Address _____

_____

Company _____

Address _____

_____

Company _____

Address _____

_____

Company _____

Address _____

_____

Company _____

Address _____

_____

Company _____

Address _____

_____

Company _____

Address _____

_____

Company _____

Address. _____

_____

NOTES

NOTES

VI

<u>INSURANCE POLICIES</u>

The following insurance policies are
essential for settling my estate.

VI. INSURANCE POLICIES

LIFE

Life insurance _____

Address _____

_____ Phone _____

Policy number _____

Life insurance _____

Address _____

_____ Phone _____

Policy number _____

Life insurance _____

Address _____

_____ Phone _____

Policy number _____

Life insurance _____

Address _____

_____ Phone _____

Policy number _____

Life insurance _____

Address _____

_____ Phone _____

Policy number _____

Life insurance _____

Address _____

_____ Phone _____

Policy number _____

Life insurance _____

Address _____

_____ Phone _____

Policy number _____

Life insurance _____

Address _____

_____ Phone _____

Policy number _____

Life insurance _____

Address _____

_____ Phone _____

Policy number _____

Life insurance _____

Address _____

_____ Phone _____

Policy number _____

Life insurance _____

Address _____

_____ Phone _____

Policy number _____

Life insurance _____

Address _____

_____ Phone _____

Policy number _____

Life insurance _____

Address _____

_____ Phone _____

Policy number _____

PROPERTY

Homeowner's insurance _____

Address _____

_____ Phone _____

Policy number _____

Homeowner's insurance _____

Address _____

_____ Phone _____

Policy number _____

Homeowner's insurance _____

Address _____

_____ Phone _____

Policy number _____

Business insurance _____

Address _____

_____ Phone _____

Policy number _____

Business insurance _____

Address _____

_____ Phone _____

Policy number _____

Business insurance _____

Address _____

_____ Phone _____

Policy number _____

Investment property insurance _____

Address _____

_____ Phone _____

Policy number _____

PROPERTY -
(Continued)

Investment property insurance _____

Address _____

_____ Phone _____

Policy number _____

Investment property insurance _____

Address _____

_____ Phone _____

Policy number _____

Investment property insurance _____

Address _____

_____ Phone _____

Policy number _____

Investment property insurance _____

Address _____

_____ Phone _____

Policy number _____

Investment property insurance _____

Address _____

_____ Phone _____

Policy number _____

HEALTH

Health insurance _____

Address _____

_____ Phone _____

Policy number _____

Health insurance _____

Address _____

_____ Phone _____

Policy number _____

AUTO-MOBILE

Automobile insurance _____

Address _____

_____ Phone _____

Policy number _____

Automobile insurance _____

Address _____

_____ Phone _____

Policy number _____

Automobile insurance _____

Address _____

_____ Phone _____

Policy number _____

Automobile insurance _____

Address _____

_____ Phone _____

Policy number _____

OTHER POLICIES

Other insurance _____

Address _____

_____ Phone _____

Policy number _____

Other insurance _____

Address _____

_____ Phone _____

Policy number _____

Other insurance _____

Address _____

_____ Phone _____

Policy number _____

NOTES

NOTES

NOTES

VII

ORGANIZATIONS AND CLUBS

I belong to the organizations and clubs
listed below. Please contact them.

VII. ORGANIZATIONS AND CLUBS

ORGANIZA-TIONS

Name _____

Address _____

_____ Phone _____

Name _____

Address _____

_____ Phone _____

Name _____

Address _____

_____ Phone _____

Name _____

Address _____

_____ Phone _____

Name _____

Address _____

_____ Phone _____

Name _____

Address _____

_____ Phone _____

Name _____

Address _____

_____ Phone _____

Name _____

Address _____

_____ Phone _____

Name_____

Address _____

_____ Phone _____

Name_____

Address _____

_____ Phone _____

Name_____

Address _____

_____ Phone _____

Name_____

Address _____

_____ Phone _____

Name_____

Address _____

_____ Phone _____

Name_____

Address _____

_____ Phone _____

Name_____

Address _____

_____ Phone _____

Name_____

Address _____

_____ Phone _____

Name_____

Address _____

_____ Phone _____

NOTES

NOTES

VIII

POSSESSIONS

It is important to know not only
what I have, but *where* to find it.
Here is a description of my belongings,
their locations, and the people I wish to
receive them.
Some states require the transfer of
personal property to be in your will or
by other written documents.

VIII. POSSESSIONS

JEWELRY

Description: _____
For: _____

Description: _____
For: _____

Description: _____
For: _____

Description: _____
For: _____

Description: _____
For: _____

Description: _____
For: _____

Description: _____
For: _____

CLOTHING

Description: _____
For: _____

Description: _____
For: _____

Description: _____
For: _____

Description: _____
For: _____

Description: _____
For: _____

SPORTS EQUIPMENT

Description: _____
For: _____

Description: _____
For: _____

Description: _____
For: _____

Description: _____
For: _____

AUTOMOBILES

Description: _____
For: _____

Description: _____
For: _____

SILVERWARE, DISHES, CRYSTAL

Description: _____
For: _____

Description: _____
For: _____

Description: _____
For: _____

Description: _____
For: _____

Description: _____
For: _____

Description: _____
For: _____

COMPUTER

Description: _____
For: _____

FURNITURE

Description: _____

For: _____

Description: _____

For: _____

Description: _____

For: _____

COLLECTOR'S ITEMS

Description: _____

For: _____

Description: _____

For: _____

Description: _____

For: _____

MISCELLANEOUS

Description: _____

For: _____

Description: _____

For: _____

Description: _____

For: _____

Description: _____

For: _____

Description: _____

For: _____

Description: _____

For: _____

IX

<u>MEMORIES TO SHARE</u>

I have some thoughts that are
special to me and I want to share these
thoughts with my loved ones.

IX. MEMORIES TO SHARE

POEMS

_____
_____
_____
_____
_____
_____
_____
_____
_____
_____
_____
_____
_____
_____
_____
_____
_____
_____
_____
_____
_____
_____
_____
_____
_____
_____
_____
_____

SAYINGS

OTHER

NOTES

NOTES

NOTES

It is with care and concern I have completed

this book to help you, my survivors,

through this difficult time of adjustment.

Signature _____